To My Dearest Matey

Jo

Something to help you on

life's merry way!

Happy Christmas with

much love from

Debs

xxxx

The
SECRET
THOUGHTS
of
MEN

Grrrr...

First published in 1996

Copyright Steven Appleby © 1996

The moral right of the author
has been asserted...

Bloomsbury Publishing PLC
2 Soho Square, London W1V 6HB

ISBN 0 7475 2969 8

Printed in Great Britain by
St Edmundsbury Press, Suffolk

€ by
Steven
Appleby

AGE 20

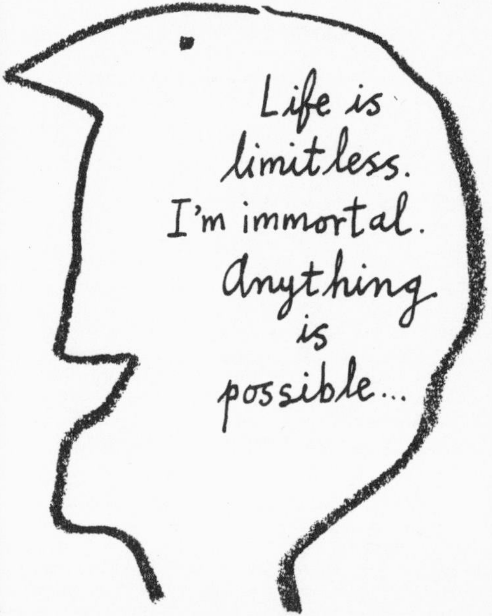

AGE 25

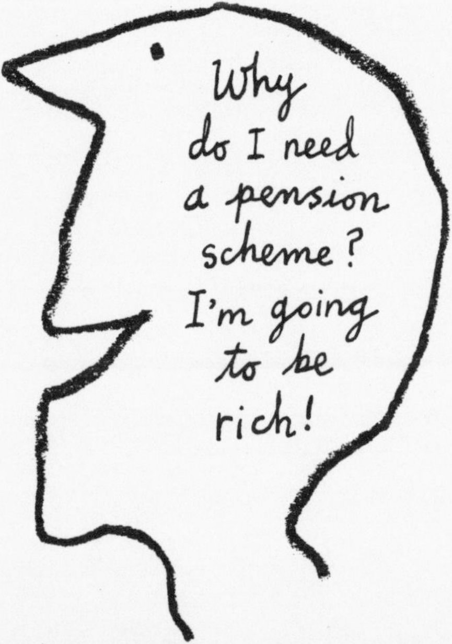

AGE 30

Life's not halfway through... There's still plenty of time... I can do anything...

AGE 40

Life's not going quite according to plan, but bags of time left... Things can still change...

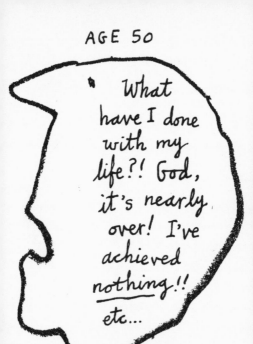

I wonder
if girls
think I'm
good-
looking...

Oh how dreadful...
Poor, poor you...
I'm saying that so you'll think I'm a nice person.

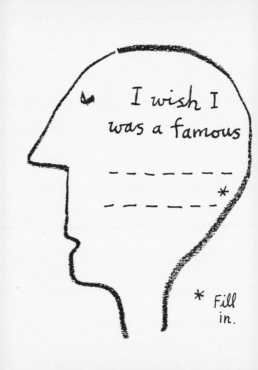

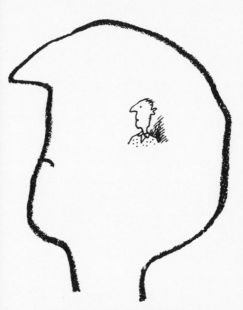

SMALL-MINDED

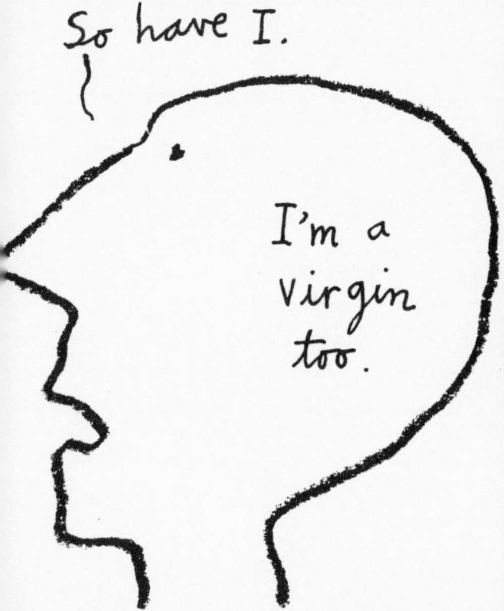
So have I.
I'm a virgin too.

Ho ho... me neither. Ugh!
Except for that time with John. And Stewart... And...

THOUGHTS TOO
EMBARRASSING TO
VOICE ALOUD:

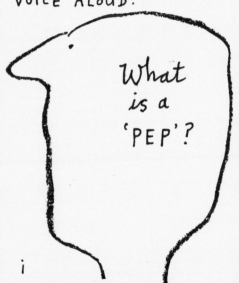

What
is a
'PEP'?

i

Is it
FA cup
final day?
Which
teams are
playing?

ii

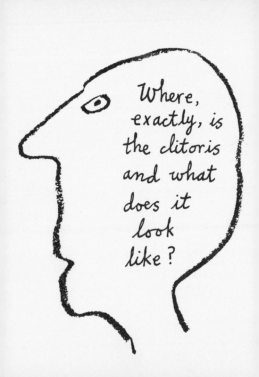

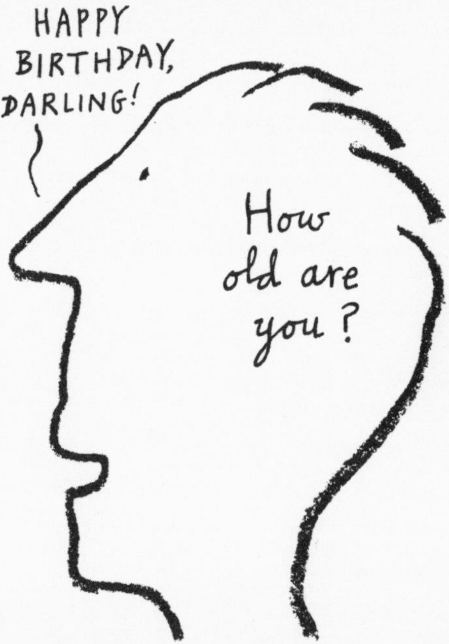
HAPPY BIRTHDAY, DARLING!
How old are you?

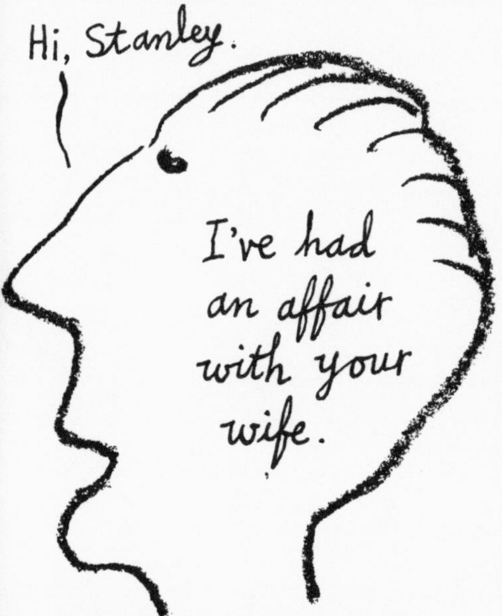
Hi, Stanley.
I've had an affair with your wife.

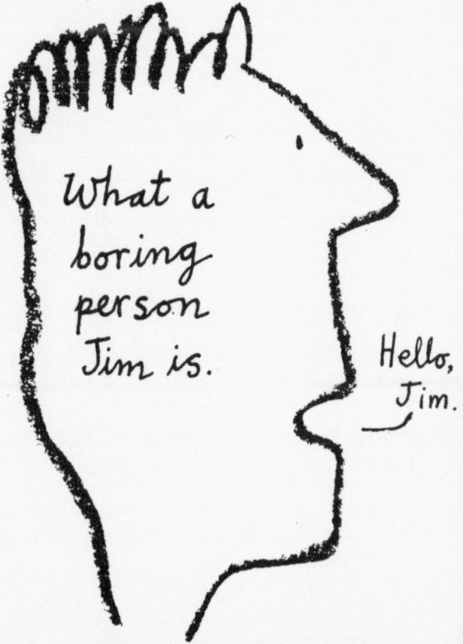
What a boring person Jim is.
Hello, Jim.

I have a horrible suspicion that I'm a boring person.
Hello, Bob.

Do you love me?
Yes.
No...
Maybe...
Don't know...
Perhaps...
But I do want to have sex with you.

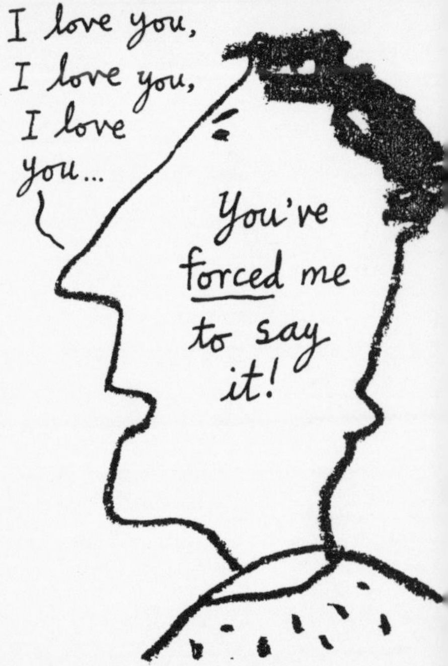
I love you,
I love you,
I love
you...
You've
forced me
to say
it!

Do you really?
Of course...
not. But I don't want to hurt your feelings.

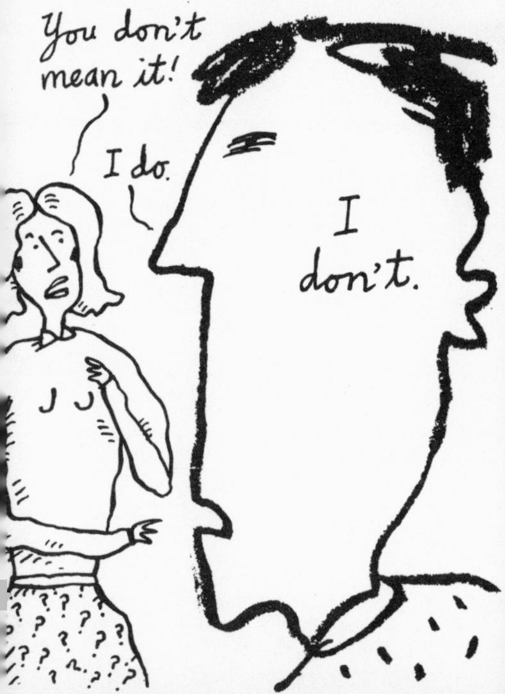
You don't mean it!
I do.
I don't.

Nosepicking time!
Now that we're married I don't need to try anymore.

my
wife
doesn't know
I'm here
wearing only
a rubber
helmet.

Why do I feel attracted to other women when I'm happily married?

Can men and women be friends without sex getting in the way?
Yes indeed!

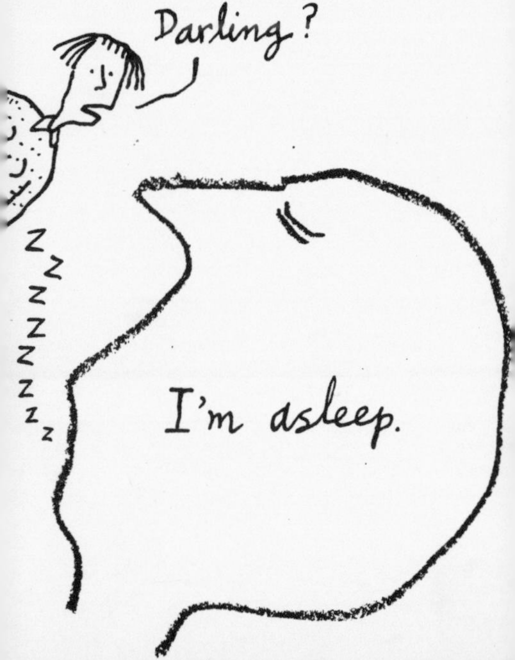
Darling?
I'm asleep.
Z Z Z Z Z Z Z z

I
wonder
what it
would
be like
to
murder
someone...

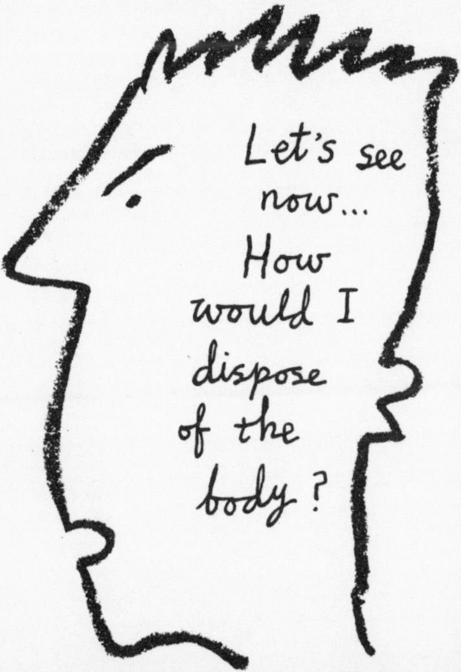
Let's see now... How would I dispose of the body?

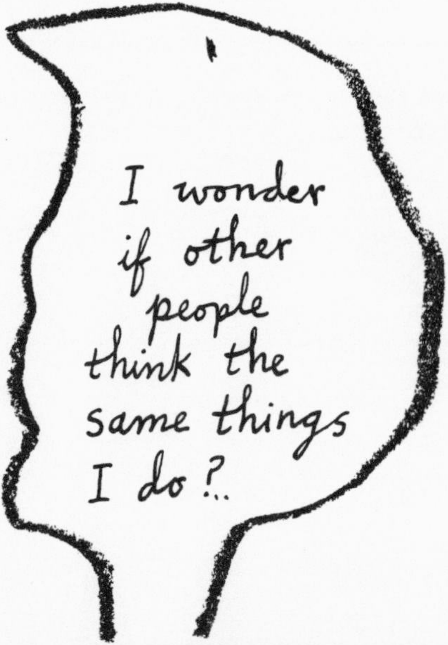
I wonder if other people think the same things I do?..

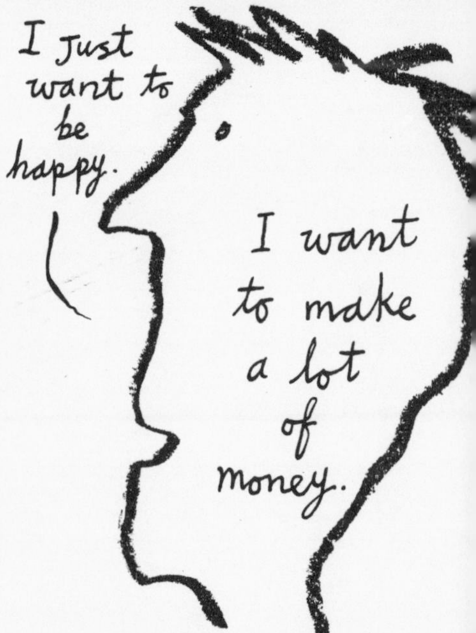
I Just want to be happy.
I want to make a lot of money.

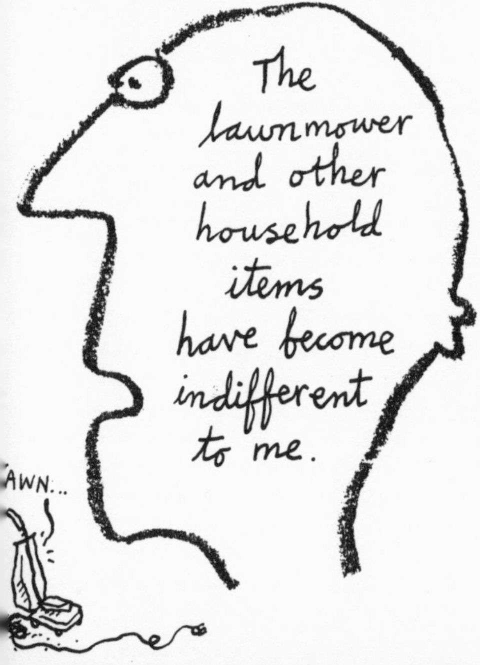
The lawnmower and other household items have become indifferent to me.
AWN...

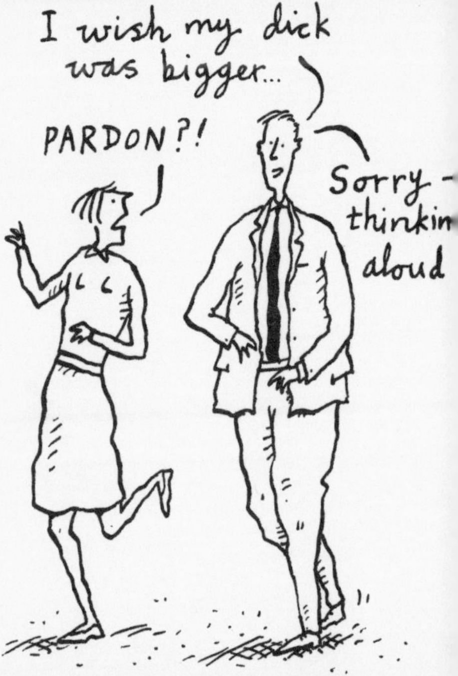
I wish my dick was bigger...
PARDON?!
Sorry - thinkin aloud

Of course, it's well known that women suffer from penis envy.

They wouldn't envy mine if they knew how small it is.

Meet Roger. He's really sensitive. A new man.
Hi.
You lucky thing, Fiona
Hi, Roger
God. Look at those tits!

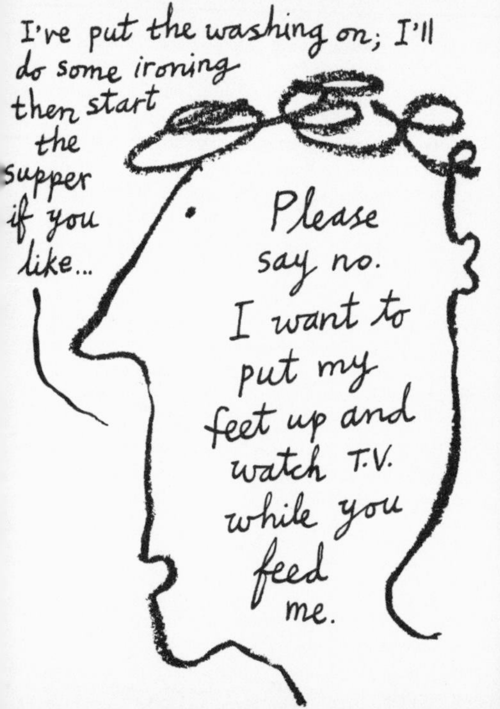
I've put the washing on; I'll do some ironing then start the supper if you like...
Please say no. I want to put my feet up and watch T.V. while you feed me.

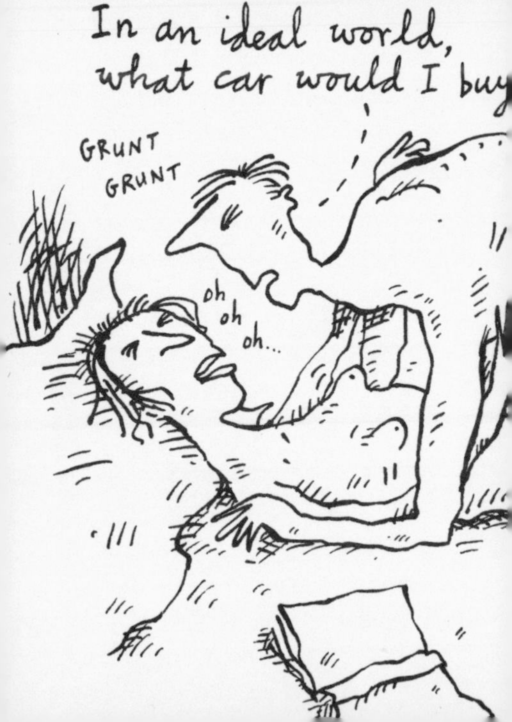
In an ideal world,
what car would I buy
GRUNT
GRUNT
oh
oh
oh...

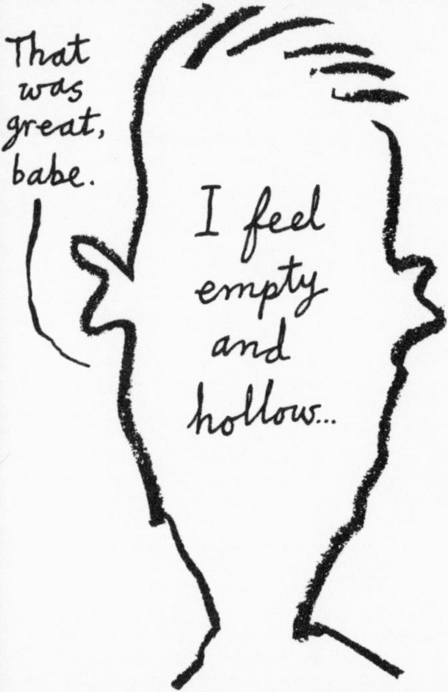
That was great, babe.
I feel empty and hollow...

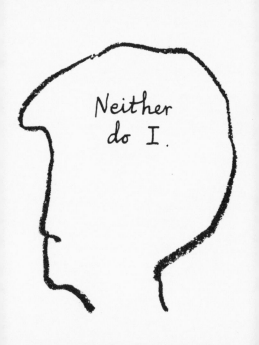

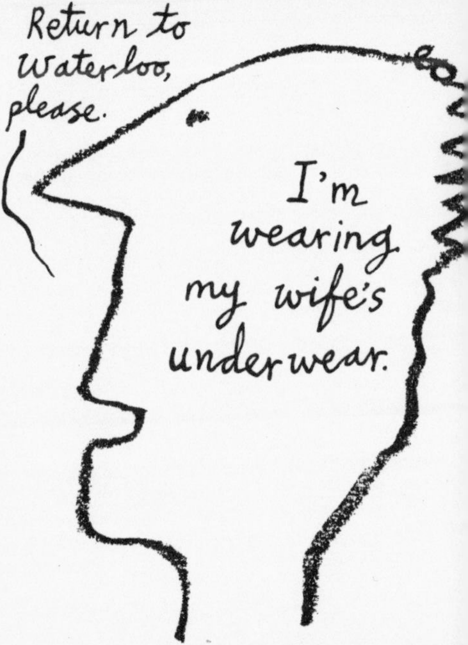
Return to Waterloo, please.
I'm wearing my wife's underwear.

I
hope I
don't get
knocked down
by a car
and need to
have my
clothing
cut
off...

My family are the most important thing in my life.

The children? My wife looks after them.

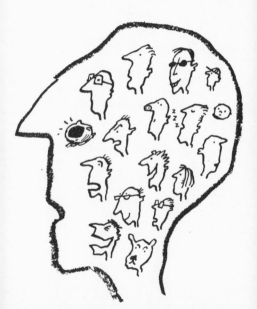

MULTIPLE PERSONALITY

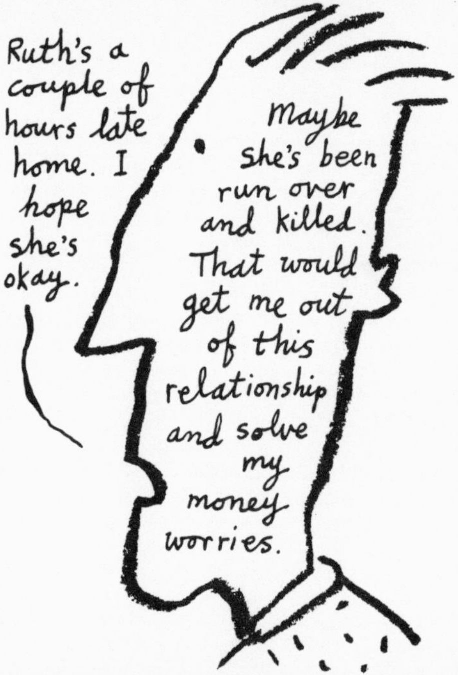
Ruth's a couple of hours late home. I hope she's okay.
Maybe she's been run over and killed. That would get me out of this relationship and solve my money worries.

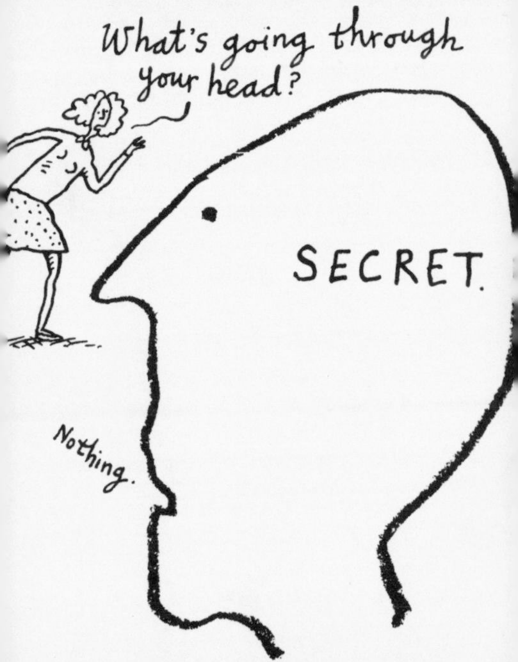
What's going through your head?
SECRET.
Nothing.